"Let's go for a ride," said Mum.

“Where to?” said Ben.

“You will see,” said Dad.
“Come on.”

"This is fun," said Liz.

"I like it here."

"Look," said Ben.
"I like the duck."

"Ben likes the duck," said Mum.

"Here," said Dad.
"This is for you."

"Let's go on a ride," said Liz.

“But the duck will not like it,” said Ben.

“Come with me, Ben,” said Liz.

"This is fun. I like it," said Ben.
"I can see a park."

Hook a duck

"No! Stop!" said Ben.

"Can you get it, Dad?"

"I can't get it," said Dad.

“Can I look for it?” said Ben.

“No, let’s go home, Ben,”
said Mum.
“We can’t see the duck.”

“Look. Ben’s duck is here.

I will get it down,” said Mum.